© 2012, 2016 Age of Learning, Inc.
Published by Age of Learning, Inc., P.O. Box 10458, Glendale, California 91209.
No part of this work may be reproduced in whole or in part, or stored in a retrieval system,
or transmitted in any form or by any means, electronic, mechanical, photocopying,
recording, or otherwise, without written permission of the publisher.
ABCmouse.com and associated logos are trademarks and/or
registered trademarks of Age of Learning, Inc.

Library of Congress Cataloging-in-Publication Data
The Grasshopper and the Ants/Age of Learning, Inc.
Summary: A carefree grasshopper learns about the importance of preparing
for the future from a colony of ants.

ISBN: 978-1-62116-004-5
Library of Congress Control Number: 2012912045

21 20 19 18 17 16 15 14 13 12   3 4 5
Printed in the U.S.A., on 10% recycled paper. ♻

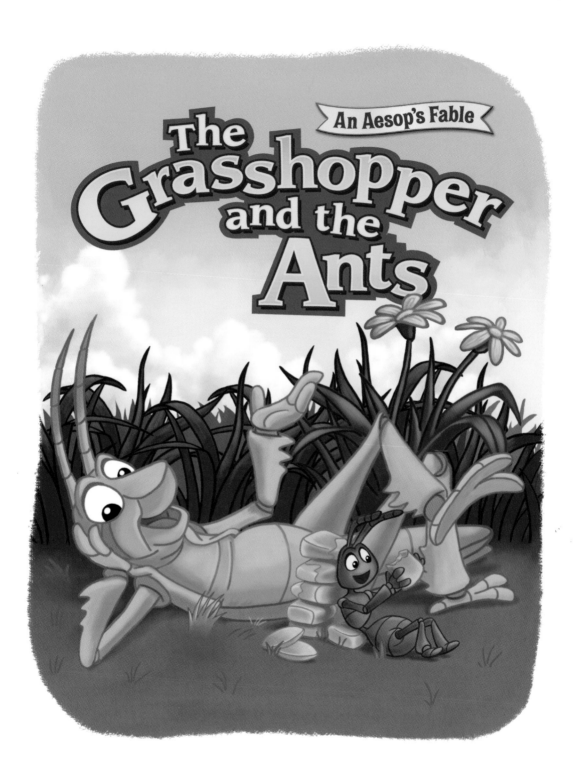

An Aesop's Fable

The Grasshopper and the Ants

Age of Learning, Inc., Glendale, California
This book is also available at **ABCmouse.com**, the award-winning early learning online curriculum.

Aesop's Fables

What are Aesop's fables?

Legend tells us that Aesop lived a very long time ago in a place called Greece and became famous for telling stories that were intended to teach lessons about life. We call his stories Aesop's fables.

The Grasshopper and the Ants

One warm spring day, a grasshopper was playing in a grassy green field when he noticed a line of ants marching along carrying some seeds.

"Where are you going with that big load?" the grasshopper asked one of them.

"We're taking these seeds to our nest," squeaked the ant.

"But it's such a beautiful day," said the grasshopper. "Come and have fun with me."

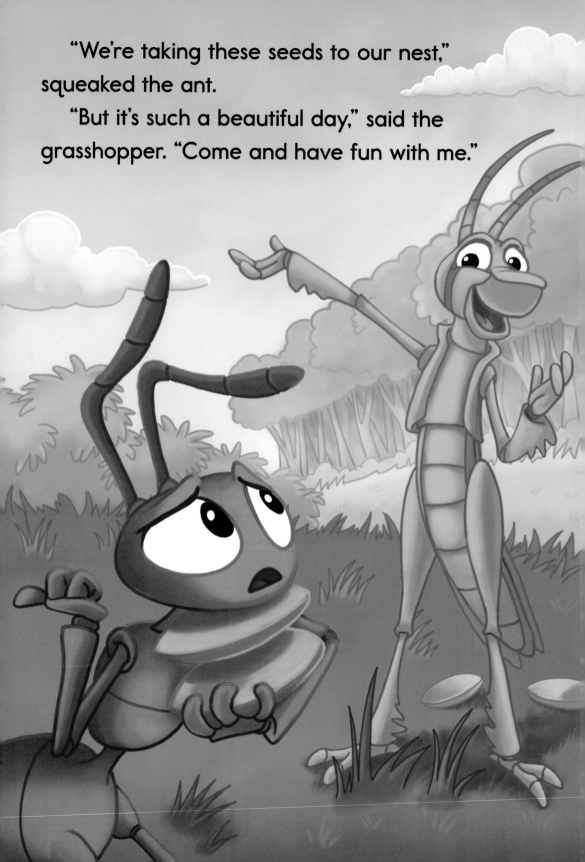

"No," said the ant. "I think you should come work with us. It's going to be a long winter, with lots of snow. You had better start storing your food now!"

"Why worry about the winter? It's only spring, and there is lots of food everywhere," said the grasshopper as he chewed on a tasty leaf.

All through the spring, the grasshopper did nothing except eat, sleep, and play. He became quite fat.

One day during the summer, the grasshopper saw the long line of ants again. They were all carrying grains of wheat.

"Where are all of you going with that food?" the grasshopper asked.

"We are taking it to our nest to save for winter," said one of the ants. "You should gather some wheat, too. It's going to be a long winter, with lots of snow."

"I have all the food that I need right now," said the grasshopper. "Why worry about winter? It's still summer!"

All summer, the grasshopper did nothing but eat, sleep, and play. He became even fatter!

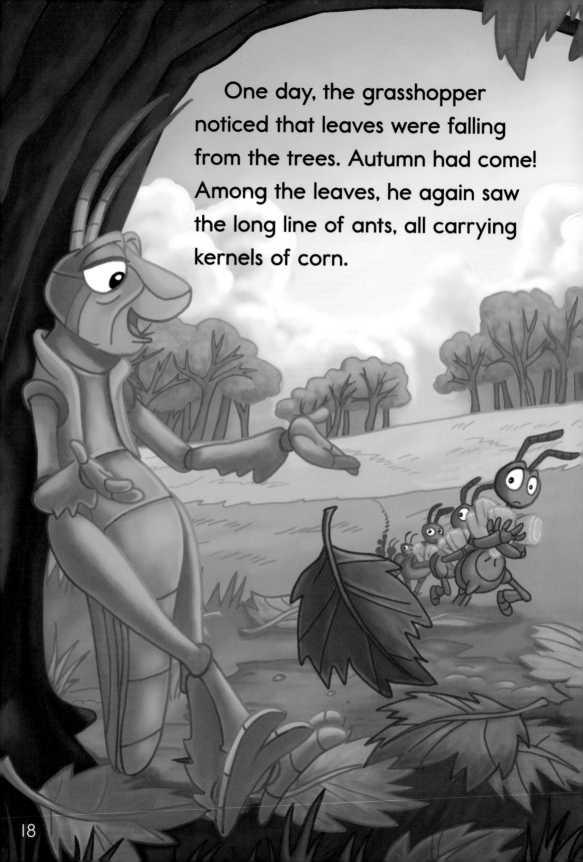

One day, the grasshopper noticed that leaves were falling from the trees. Autumn had come! Among the leaves, he again saw the long line of ants, all carrying kernels of corn.

"Where are you going with that corn?" the grasshopper asked one of the ants.

The ant replied, "We are taking it to our nest to save for winter. You should gather some corn, too. It's going to be a long winter, with lots of snow."

"That's too much work," said the grasshopper.
"Winter is not here yet, and when it comes, I am
sure I will be able to find some food."

A few weeks later, winter came, and the snow began to fall. Just as the ants had predicted, the snow was very deep. This was not a problem for the ants, though. They were all snug in their nest with lots of good food to eat.

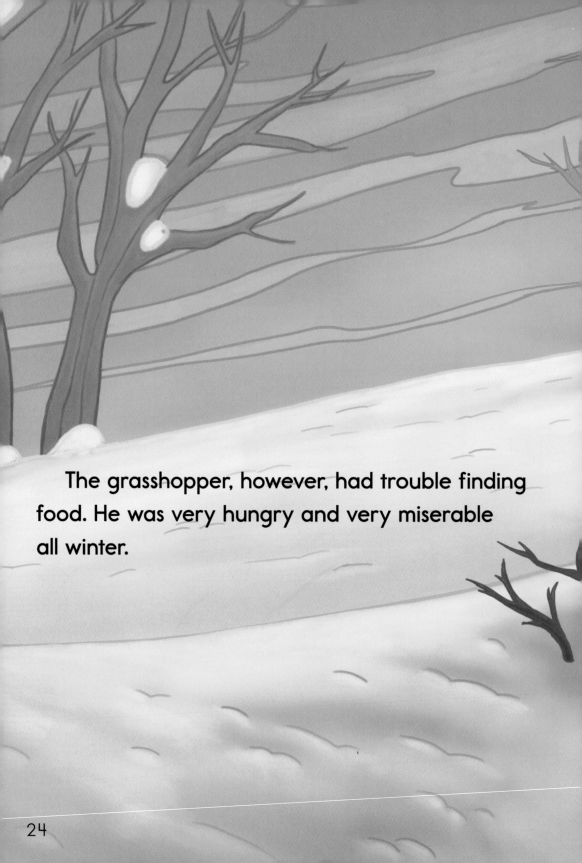

The grasshopper, however, had trouble finding food. He was very hungry and very miserable all winter.

By the time winter ended, the grasshopper had learned a valuable lesson: It is important to prepare for the future.

The End

Moral of the Story
Work today for what you will need tomorrow.

Glossary

fable Definition: A **fable** is a short story that is intended to teach a lesson. **Example:** We call his stories Aesop's **fables**.

gather Definition: When you **gather** things, you bring them all together in one place. **Example:** You should **gather** some wheat, too. It's going to be a long winter, with lots of snow.

grain Definition: A **grain** is a small seed that people and animals can eat, and it can also be used to make bread, cereal, and other foods. People sometimes grind up **grain** into a powder called *flour*. **Example:** One day in the summer, the grasshopper saw the long line of ants again. They were all carrying **grains** of wheat.

Greece Definition: **Greece** is a country in Europe that has many islands, mountains, and beaches. It has existed for thousands of years. **Example:** Legend tells us that Aesop lived a very long time ago in a place called **Greece**.

kernel Definition: A **kernel** is another word for a single grain. **Example:** Among the leaves, he again saw the long line of ants, all carrying **kernels** of corn.

legend Definition: A **legend** is a story from long ago. **Legends** usually have events that could happen and other events that could not really happen. **Example:** **Legend** tells us that Aesop lived a very long time ago in a place called Greece.

Glossary

lesson **Definition:** A **lesson** is something that a person is supposed to learn. **Example:** By the time winter ended, the grasshopper had learned a valuable **lesson:** It is important to prepare for the future.

moral **Definition:** The **moral** of a story is the lesson the reader is supposed to learn from the story. **Example:** Moral of the story: Work today for what you will need tomorrow.

predict **Definition:** When you **predict** something, you say what you think is going to happen in the future. **Example:** Just as the ants had **predicted**, the snow was very deep.

prepare **Definition:** When you **prepare**, you get ready for something that is going to happen. **Example:** By the time winter ended, the grasshopper had learned a valuable lesson: It is important to **prepare** for the future.

snug **Definition:** If you are **snug**, you feel comfortable and safe in a place. **Example:** They were all **snug** in their nest with lots of good food to eat.

store **Definition:** When you **store** something, you put it in a place where it is safe and where you can use it later. **Example:** "No," said the ant. "I think you should come work with us. It's going to be a long winter, with lots of snow. You had better start **storing** your food now!"